SLIMY STICKY STINKY SCIENCE

Compiled by Megan Stieg and Tammi Salzano
Illustrated and designed by Cameron Thorp

an imprint of
■SCHOLASTIC
www.scholastic.com

Published by Tangerine Press, an imprint of Scholastic Inc., 557 Broadway; New York, NY 10012

Scholastic Australia Pty. Ltd **Scholastic New Zealand** **Scholastic UK**
Gosford, NSW   Greenmount, Auckland   Coventry, Warwickshire

10 9 8 7 6 5 4 3 2 1
ISBN-10: 0-545-01432-8
ISBN-13: 978-0-545-01432-8

Made in China

CONTENTS

WELCOME TO THE WORLD OF SCIENCE!

Let's see: Petri dish, test tube, dropper…Oh, hello there! I'm Newton, scientist extraordinaire. I was just getting my laboratory ready for today's experiments when you stopped by. And lucky you; you're just in time to help! I'm always looking for victims—er, I mean, volunteers—to assist with my latest and greatest experiments. So, if you love slimy, sticky, stinky science experiments (and who doesn't?), you've come to the right place!

Before we get started, I need to tell you that even though I am a scientist extraordinaire and can make things bubble and spill over with the best of them, I'm not very good at explaining the real science behind an experiment. So, I brought along another scientist who can give you the scoop on the technical stuff. After you do an experiment, don't forget to read the explanation! My scientist put a lot of effort into explaining things so that young scientists like yourselves (and, okay, yours truly) could understand.

Are you ready to get your hands dirty?
Follow me into the fun world of slimy, sticky,
stinky science!

Stuff in This Kit

Successful scientists need STUFF. And as a scientist, I'm always looking for new STUFF, and now my lab is filled with STUFF. (I can't find half the STUFF I need on any given day, but that's another story.) Luckily for you, your kit came with lots of equipment you'll need to do some cool experiments. You'll also need to grab a few things from around the house, so be sure to ask a grownup helper for the supplies you'll need. Here's what you get in your kit:

GLOW-IN-THE-DARK SLIME POWDER
You'll use the glow-in-the-dark slime powder for the experiment on pages 10–11.

TEST TUBE
The test tube in this kit has liquid millimeter measurements printed on the sides. You'll use these markings to measure things in some experiments.

TEST TUBE CAP
To seal your test tube, put the cap on top and press until it snaps closed.

DIAPER DUST
You'll use the diaper dust for the experiment on pages 14–15.

PETRI DISH
You'll use the Petri dish for a few of the experiments.

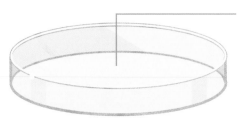

WOODEN SCRAPER
You'll need the wooden scraper for the experiment on pages 50–51.

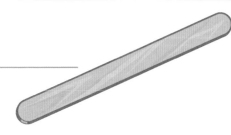

DROPPER

The dropper helps you to move liquids from place to place.

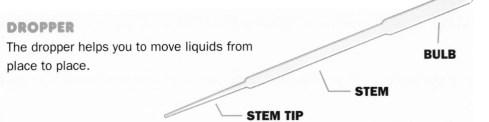

BULB

STEM

STEM TIP

Filling the dropper:
Put the stem tip into liquid. Squeeze and release the bulb. The liquid will be sucked into the dropper.

Emptying the dropper:
Put the stem tip where you want the liquid to drop. Squeeze the bulb.

STICKY ALIEN
You'll need the sticky alien for the experiment on pages 22–23.

EXPERIMENT TRAY
The experiment tray includes all these things:

• Punch-out measuring spoon:
  The measuring spoon is two-sided. The instructions refer to the two sides as the large or small measuring spoon. Have a grownup help you trim the edges of the small spoon with scissors to make it fit inside the test tube.

• Round pits: You'll use these pits for the experiment on pages 44–45.

• Rectangular basin: You'll use this basin for the experiment on pages 56–57.

You also have a test tube holder in the container that has all the components in your kit. Poke the rounded end of your test tube into this holder to make your test tube stand up.

Way Too Much Information about Safety and Cleanliness

There's a phrase that goes, "You learn from your mistakes." And that's very true when we're talking about science. But when it comes to SAFETY and CLEANLINESS in the lab, there's no room for mistakes. So, before we dive in, I need to share some tips with you to help keep you safe in the lab. You wouldn't go skydiving without a parachute, would you? (Well, maybe you adventurous types out there would.) Put it this way—you SHOULDN'T go skydiving without a parachute. In the same way, you ABSOLUTELY SHOULDN'T conduct any kind of science experiment without following the rules of safety and cleanliness.

SAFETY FIRST!

- Follow the instructions carefully, and don't try to make up experiments. Some common household materials can produce harmful vapors when they are mixed together.

- Wear goggles to protect your eyes from splashing liquids. You can pick up an inexpensive pair of goggles from your local home improvement store.

- Don't eat or drink the results of the experiments in this book. Any food you use should be thrown away at the end of the experiment.

- Wash your hands after each experiment. Nothing used in this book will harm you, but it's better to be safe than sorry.

- If the instructions tell you to get a grownup helper, GET A GROWNUP HELPER! Sure, independence is great, but it's not worth it if you get hurt.

KEEP IT CLEAN!

• Many of the experiments in this book are MESSY so, again, getting the okay from Mom or Dad is a must! Work on a countertop near the kitchen sink, if possible, and completely cover your work area with newspaper. You might also considering wearing an apron or an old T-shirt that you don't mind ruining.

• Clean up your equipment after every experiment. If your equipment is dirty, your next experiment might not work.

• To rinse your dropper, hold the tip in clean water. Squeeze and release the bulb several times.

• It's safe to flush any of the liquids used in these experiments down the drain. Just let the tap run until the sink is clean.

• Don't flush any of the solid or semi-solid materials (including slime and goop) down the drain. Put these things in a plastic bag and toss them in the trash can.

I THINK THAT'S IT. ON TO THE EXPERIMENTS! ☞

Slimy, Sticky Stuff:
Shimmering Slime

Not only is the stuff in this experiment slimy, it actually GLOWS IN THE DARK. Cool, huh? One thing's for sure—you'll never lose this stuff, not even when your room is pitch black!

What you need
- **Glow-in-the-dark slime powder** (green powder in your kit)
- **Resealable plastic bag**
- **Test tube**
- **Water**

WHAT YOU DO

1. Dump all of the slime powder into the resealable plastic bag.

2. Pour two FULL (all the way to the top) test tubes of water into the bag. Squeeze gently until the powder and water combine and form a slippery slime.

3. Grab a handful of slime. (One hand only—keep the other one clean in case you need to open doors, flip light switches, etc.) Smear the stuff all over your palm and fingers.

4. Hold your slimy hand under a bright light for about a minute.

5. Go someplace dark and look at your hand. YIKES! It's glowing a sickly green!

TRY THIS

Put the entire bag of slime under a light for a minute or so. Take it into a dark place and admire the bright glow. Leave the bag in the dark place for about half an hour, then go back and check on it. Now the glow is BARELY THERE.

AND NOW THE SCIENTIFIC SCOOP

Your glow-in-the-dark slime is a polymer—a substance with molecules linked into long chains. The slime is sticky and clingy and slimy because all those long chains stop the slime from moving quickly. Plus, this slime is special in another way: it contains a material that absorbs light energy. When you take the slime into a dark place, it starts to release the energy it absorbed. The released energy can be seen as a visible light.

Toe-Cheese Goop

The name of this experiment is a little misleading, if you ask me. I mean, when I hear the word CHEESE, I think of cheddar, mozzarella, and Swiss. But this toe-cheese stuff isn't really cheese at all. It's tough, springy, and completely inedible. It might be a neat science experiment, but it sure doesn't make much of a snack for a hungry scientist. NO EATING!

What you need

- Large measuring spoon
- Water
- White glue
- 2 disposable cups
- Food coloring
- Stirring spoons
- Borax

WHAT YOU DO

1. Put six large measuring spoonfuls each of water and glue into one of the cups. Add a few drops of food coloring. Mix well.

2. In the other cup, mix one large measuring spoonful of borax and ¼ cup (59 ml) of water.

3. Put four large measuring spoonfuls of the borax mixture into the glue mixture. Stir well—if you can! Very quickly, the liquids gel into a DISGUSTING, STICKY BLOB!

TRY THIS

Squeeze the Toe-Cheese Goop between two paper towels to remove extra liquid. The result is an even thicker, springier BLOB OF GOO.

AND NOW THE SCIENTIFIC SCOOP

Toe-Cheese Goop is another polymer. The borax molecules connect the glue molecules to form the tangled chains in this squishy substance.

Diaper Slime-O-Rama

The white powder you'll be using in this experiment is the same stuff that sucks up moisture in baby diapers. Check it out!

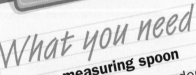

What you need

- **Large measuring spoon**
- **Diaper dust** (white powder in your kit)
- **Resealable plastic bag**
- **Water**

WHAT YOU DO

1. Put one large measuring spoonful of diaper dust into the resealable plastic bag.

2. Little by little, add water to the bag. Every time you add more water, squeeze the bag to mix the stuff inside.

3. Keep adding water and squeezing until you feel your slime is perfect. (Not to ruin the surprise, but you'll be AMAZED at how much water you can add.) When you're done, grab a handful of goo and give it a good SQUISH!

TRY THIS

If you use up all your diaper dust, you can get more from a regular baby diaper. Have an adult cut the diaper into strips and put the strips into a bag. SHAKE, SHAKE, SHAKE until a bunch of white powder falls to the bottom of the bag. That's your diaper dust!

AND NOW THE SCIENTIFIC SCOOP

The diaper dust granules are made of a polymer that can absorb up to 30 times its own weight in water. As the polymer absorbs more and more water, it becomes gooier and gooier.

Disappearing Slime

I don't like to get too upset about things. "EASY COME, EASY GO," I always say. You might want to adopt this attitude, too. Because you know that cool goop you made in the last experiment? It's about to DISAPPEAR. Say ADIOS, AMIGOS.

What you need

- **Diaper Slime-O-Rama** (pages 14–15)
- **Plate**
- **Salt**

WHAT YOU DO

1. Drop a big handful of Diaper Slime-O-Rama onto a plate.

2. Generously shake salt all over the slime. Sit back and wait for the fun to start. After about a minute, the slime starts to SLUMP, and water begins oozing out. A few minutes later, the slime is practically GONE!

TRY THIS

There's another easy way to make your slime disappear. Put a big blob on a plate and set it in direct sunlight. How long does it take for the slime to turn back into powder?

AND NOW THE SCIENTIFIC SCOOP

Diaper Slime-O-Rama is so amazing, it's like SUPER SLIME. But like all super beings, your slime has a fatal weakness. No, it's not kryptonite. Your slime can't handle SALT. Salt weakens the polymer bonds and reduces the amount of liquid the powder can hold.

Greasy, Grimy Gopher Guts

I've never personally seen a gopher's guts, but I'm willing to bet that they're greasy and grimy—just like the stuff you're going to make in this experiment.

What you need

- White glue
- Green food coloring
- Two disposable cups
- Stirring spoon
- Liquid laundry starch

WHAT YOU DO

1. Mix a big glob of white glue and a few drops of green food coloring in a disposable cup.

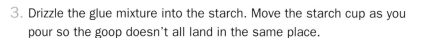

2. Fill another disposable cup about halfway with liquid laundry starch.

3. Drizzle the glue mixture into the starch. Move the starch cup as you pour so the goop doesn't all land in the same place.

4. Reach into the starch and pull out the GOPHER GUTS. They're smelly, slippery, stringy, and dripping with SLIME. Ugh!

TRY THIS

Put the Gopher Guts into a resealable plastic bag and freeze them. Not only do they feel nasty, the cold keeps them from "decomposing."

AND NOW THE SCIENTIFIC SCOOP

The molecules in the liquid laundry starch connect the glue molecules to make these tough, intestine-like strands. Here's a hint: the Gopher Guts are safe to handle, but you should wash your hands after touching them. (Yeah, like you were going to leave that disgusting stuff on your skin.)

Slippery Sludge

I love a good, slimy experiment just as much as the next scientist, but this Slippery Sludge is even too slimy for ME. Enjoy!

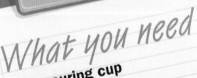

What you need

- Measuring cup
- Cornstarch
- Resealable plastic bag
- Light corn syrup
- Dropper
- Water
- Blue food coloring

WHAT YOU DO

1. Pour ½ cup (118 ml) of cornstarch into the plastic bag.

2. Add ¼ cup (59 ml) of corn syrup, a dropperful of water, and several drops of blue food coloring.

3. Seal the bag and knead the ingredients until they're all mixed together. If it's too dry, add a little more corn syrup. If it's too wet, add a little more cornstarch.

4. Reach in and grab a sticky handful. Ew!

AND NOW THE SCIENTIFIC SCOOP

This mixture is another polymer. The cornstarch and corn syrup connect to make the slippery, sticky chains in this substance.

Sticky Alien

You're probably wondering why we've thrown an experiment like this in the middle of our slippery, slimy lab work. I mean, an ALIEN? This just goes to show you that we scientists cater to EVERYONE—even extraterrestrials.

What you need

- **Sticky alien in your kit**
- **Wall** (painted with non-glossy paint)
- **Window**

WHAT YOU DO

1. Throw the alien against the wall. Does it stick?

2. Now throw the alien against the window. Does it stick?

The sticky alien is intended to be used only on a window surface and a wall painted with non-glossy paint.

AND NOW THE SCIENTIFIC SCOOP

Friction is the force that resists motion between two objects. The more friction there is between two objects, the harder it is to move them. The wall and window appear smooth, but they are filled with tiny bumps. These bumps cause friction between the surfaces and the alien. The wall is rougher than the window, so it creates more friction. That's why the alien sticks to the wall, but not the window!

Brain Sludge

For this experiment, you're going to use milk to make a disgusting BRAIN that you can hold in the palm of your hand. COOL!

What you need

- Test tube in holder
- Vinegar
- Dropper
- Milk (any kind)

WHAT YOU DO

1. Fill the test tube about halfway with vinegar.

2. Fill the dropper with milk. Poke it into the test tube so the tip almost touches the bottom.

3. Squeeze the dropper. A cheesy white BRAIN begins to form in the bottom of the test tube!

TRY THIS

Hold your hand over the sink. Pour everything in the test tube into your hand. All the liquid will drip into the sink, and you'll be left holding a SHIVERING, QUIVERING blob of nastiness.

AND NOW THE SCIENTIFIC SCOOP

Milk contains a protein called casein. When milk combines with any acid, the casein separates out of the milk as curd. The vinegar in your test tube is an acid, so rubbery curds appear as soon as you start squeezing the dropper.

Hard or Soft?

That IS the question when it comes to this experiment! You're about to make some cool slime that's actually hard...no, wait, it's soft! How is that possible?

What you need

- Test tube
- Water
- Bowl
- Teaspoon
- Cornstarch

WHAT YOU DO

1. Fill the test tube to the "12" mark with water.
   Pour the water in a bowl. Repeat.

2. Add a level teaspoonful of cornstarch to the bowl and stir.
   Keep adding a little cornstarch and stirring until the slime
   slowly runs when you tip the bowl.

3. Pick up the slime and squeeze it. What happens?

AND NOW THE SCIENTIFIC SCOOP

**This slime seems like a liquid when it's
under pressure, but it becomes firmer
when it's squeezed. That's because cornstarch is a polymer, made up of long,
chainlike molecules. When you squeeze
the slime, the molecules become tangled. That's why the slime stiffens.**

Gobbledygook

just like saying this word: gobbledygook. It also can come in handy when you're explaining an experiment to a nonscience type. "Well, yes, dear observer, when I oh-so-carefully mix these items together, they create a very scientific substance called gobbledygook." Okay, so maybe it's just a fun word to say.

What you need

- Test tube and cap
- Borax
- Two bowls
- Water
- Spoon
- White glue
- Food coloring (any color)

WHAT YOU DO

1. Fill the test tube cap with borax. Pour the borax into a bowl.

2. Add three test-tubefuls of water, and stir well. Rinse the spoon.

3. In another bowl, mix or pour three test-tubefuls of white glue. Rinse the tube.

4. Add three test-tubefuls of water and five drops of food coloring to the glue. Stir well.

5. Combine the two mixtures, and then stir quickly.

6. Drain the water from the bowl, and then pull out the slime.

AND NOW THE
SCIENTIFIC SCOOP

Gobbledygook is another example of a polymer at work. The molecules in the borax connect the glue molecules to form the tangled chains in this slime.

29

Super Suction

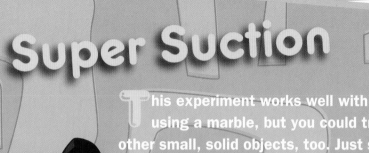

This experiment works well with using a marble, but you could try other small, solid objects, too. Just stay away from Mom's pearl necklace! She might find a way to stick YOU in the middle of this experiment.

What you need

- Gobbledygook (pages 28–29)
- Table or countertop
- Large marble

WHAT YOU DO

1. Roll the slime into a ball. Put the slime on a table or countertop. Wait about 15 seconds for the slime to flatten.

2. Push a marble about halfway into the center of the slime. Wait a few seconds.

3. Try to pull the marble out of the slime. Can you do it?

AND NOW THE SCIENTIFIC SCOOP

When you push the marble into the slime, you force out all of the air between the two materials. This creates a suction, making it difficult to remove the marble. To break the suction, pull firmly on the marble or force air between the marble and the slime by poking your finger under the marble.

Slime Rise

If you like slime (and who doesn't), you'll LOVE seeing what it can do in this next experiment.

What you need

- **Newspaper**
- **Gobbledygook** (pages 28–29)
- **Empty, clean jar** (such as a mayonnaise or pickle jar)

WHAT YOU DO

1. Cover your work surface with newspaper.

2. Roll the slime around in your hands to form a ball, and then set it on the newspaper. Rinse and dry your hands.

3. Turn the jar upside down and place it over the ball. Swirl the jar rapidly to make the ball spin up inside the jar. Carefully lift the jar and swirl it faster.

4. After a while, slow the swirling. What happens?

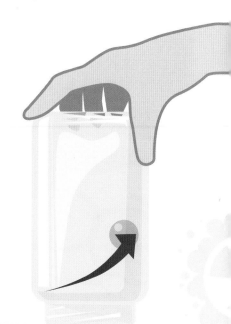

AND NOW THE SCIENTIFIC SCOOP

When you swirl the jar, the ball begins to spin. As you swirl the jar faster and faster, increased momentum slows the ball to overcome gravity and climb the inside of the jar! As you slow the swirling motion, gravity takes over, and the ball drops out of the jar.

Stop the Presses!

"Enormous Mutant Rat Escapes Lab!" Wouldn't that be a pretty funny headline? You don't think so? Well, hopefully you WILL think this experiment is fun. Just make sure you use newspaper and not your older sister's math homework. Yikes! Talk about making headlines!

What you need

- Test tube
- Liquid laundry starch
- Disposable cup
- Water
- White glue
- Spoon
- Comics section of a newspape
- Table or countertop

WHAT YOU DO

1. Fill the test tube with liquid laundry starch, and then pour the starch into a cup. Rinse the test tube with water.

2. Fill the test tube with glue, and then pour the glue into the cup. Repeat. Stir well with a spoon. Scoop the slime out of the cup and roll it around in your hands for a few minutes.

3. Lay the comics page on a table or countertop. Put the slime on top of a cartoon and press firmly. Peel off the slime and look at the bottom.

AND NOW THE SCIENTIFIC SCOOP

The slime is sticky, so it pulls the ink off the page. When you peel the slime off the newspaper, an image comes with it. You can even distort the image by stretching the slime!

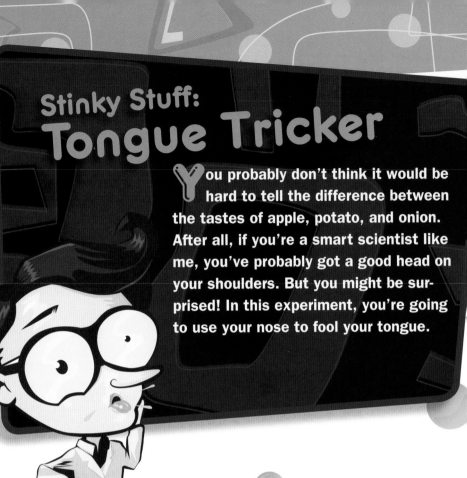

Stinky Stuff:
Tongue Tricker

You probably don't think it would be hard to tell the difference between the tastes of apple, potato, and onion. After all, if you're a smart scientist like me, you've probably got a good head on your shoulders. But you might be surprised! In this experiment, you're going to use your nose to fool your tongue.

What you need

- Grownup helper
- Apple
- Raw potato
- Raw onion

WHAT YOU DO

1. Ask your grownup helper to remove the skins from the apple, potato, and onion, and then cut a bite-sized cube from each. All the cubes should be about the same size. Make sure you keep your back turned so you can't see what your helper is doing.

2. When your helper is done, close your eyes tight and turn around to face your helper. Hold your nose with one hand. With the other, grab one of the food cubes. Stick it in your mouth and eat it. Tell your helper what kind of food you think it is (apple, potato, or onion).

3. Still closing your eyes and holding your nose, eat the other two food cubes one by one. Yummy! After you eat each cube, tell your helper what you think it was.

4. After you're done eating all three cubes, open your eyes and release your nose. Ask your helper how you did. Were you able to identify all the foods correctly?

AND NOW THE SCIENTIFIC SCOOP

Most of the flavors in food and drink are smells, not tastes. As you chew, vapors from the food in your mouth float into your nasal passages. Your nose then sends information to your brain about what kind of food you're eating. When you hold your nose, you're actually cutting off most of the taste of your food, and you may have trouble telling the difference between foods with similar textures.

A Real Bad Egg

Rotten eggs are nature's stink bombs—just one whiff is enough to send most people running! This experiment shows you how to make your own gross "essence of egg."

What you need

- Raw egg
- Mixing bowl
- Spoon
- Petri dish

WHAT YOU DO

1. Break the egg into the bowl, and then use the spoon to mix it well.

2. Pour the egg mixture into your Petri dish until it is nearly full. Place the lid on the dish.

3. Set the covered Petri dish in a sunny spot and leave it there for a day or two. You can do "smell checks" every now and then to see how your egg is progressing. Just lift the lid and take a whiff (but DON'T TOUCH!). If the egg isn't "done" yet, re-cover the dish and let it sit awhile longer. Remember, there are no absolutes in this experiment. The egg is "done" whenever you decide it's done. But the longer you leave the egg in the sun, the more rancid your results will be.

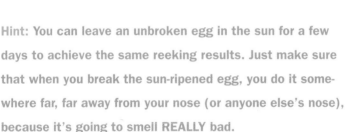

> Hint: You can leave an unbroken egg in the sun for a few days to achieve the same reeking results. Just make sure that when you break the sun-ripened egg, you do it somewhere far, far away from your nose (or anyone else's nose), because it's going to smell REALLY bad.

AND NOW THE SCIENTIFIC SCOOP

Eggs contain sulfides—smelly compounds that are a mixture of sulfur, metals, and other organic elements. The sulfides don't smell bad when the egg is fresh, but when the egg rots (a process called putrefaction), the sulfides are released as stinky gases.

Battle of the Noses

Think you've got a powerful sniffer? Here's a fun way to test the power of your nose against a friend's!

What you need

- **10 different household substances** (see on page 41 for suggestions)
- **Marker**
- **10 disposable cups**
- **Answer form** (pages 42–43)
- **A friend**
- **Table and chair**
- **Blindfold**
- **Pen or pencil**

WHAT YOU DO

Gather 10 household substances with strong, familiar scents.
Here are a few suggestions:

Coffee grinds	Lemon segments or juice	Banana	Mustard
Chocolate	Tuna fish	Peanut butter	Vanilla extract
Crushed garlic	Orange segments or juice	Toothpaste	Pine needles
Crayons	Bouillon cubes	Baby powder	Spices
Pencil shavings	Bubble gum	Ketchup	Soap

1. Use the marker to label your disposable cups 1 through 10. Then put some of each substance you've chosen into a separate cup. Write each substance's name on the "Cup contains:" lines on pages 42–43.

2. Have your friend sit at a table. Then gently blindfold your friend with a bandanna or other piece of cloth. Make sure your friend can't see anything from behind the blindfold. No fair peeking!

3. Have your friend sniff each cup. (You'll need to hand the cups to your friend, since he or she won't be able to see them.) Then ask your friend to name the scent. Write your friend's guesses on pages 42–43.

4. Grade your friend's nose by counting the number of correct answers.

5. Have your friend use the above directions to set up a smell test for you. Your friend should use different scents from the ones you picked. How did you do?

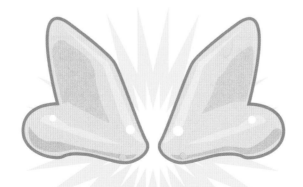

Smell Test

Instructions for using this test are given on page 41. Several spaces are provided for writing down guesses, so you can test several people at once if you like. Hint: If you test more than one person at the same time, make sure your test subjects can't hear each other's guesses. Tell your friends to whisper their answers to you.

Who will win the battle of the noses?

Cup #1 contains: _____
Name: _____ Guess: _____ Name: _____ Guess: _____
Name: _____ Guess: _____ Your guess: _____

Cup #2 contains: _____
Name: _____ Guess: _____ Name: _____ Guess: _____
Name: _____ Guess: _____ Your guess: _____

Cup #3 contains: _____
Name: _____ Guess: _____ Name: _____ Guess: _____
Name: _____ Guess: _____ Your guess: _____

Cup #4 contains: _____
Name: _____ Guess: _____ Name: _____ Guess: _____
Name: _____ Guess: _____ Your guess: _____

Cup #5 contains: _____
Name: _____ Guess: _____ Name: _____ Guess: _____
Name: _____ Guess: _____ Your guess: _____

Cup #6 contains: _____
Name: _____ Guess: _____ Name: _____ Guess: _____
Name: _____ Guess: _____ Your guess: _____

Cup #7 contains: _____
Name: _____ Guess: _____ Name: _____ Guess: _____
Name: _____ Guess: _____ Your guess: _____

Cup #8 contains: _____

Name: _____ Guess: _____ Name: _____ Guess: _____

Name: _____ Guess: _____ Your guess: _____

Cup #9 contains: _____

Name: _____ Guess: _____ Name: _____ Guess: _____

Name: _____ Guess: _____ Your guess: _____

Cup #10 contains: _____

Name: _____ Guess: _____ Name: _____ Guess: _____

Name: _____ Guess: _____ Your guess: _____

Scores

Name: _____ Correct out of 10: ____

Name: _____ Correct out of 10: ____

Name: _____ Correct out of 10: ____

You: _____ Correct out of 10: ____

How Did You Do?

9–10 Your nose is in tip-top smelling shape!

6–8 Good! Your nose knows its way around the lab.

3–5 Not too bad, but your nose could definitely use a little practice in the art of smelling!

0–2 Do you have a cold? If not, you'd better check to make sure your nose is still attached!

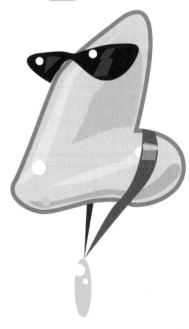

Stinky Cabbage Stew

Stinky Cabbage Stew sounds like something you might find seeping out of a garbage can in a dark alley. But this stew is cool because it has magical **COLOR-CHANGING PROPERTIES**. It turns a nifty pink or green to tell you whether things are acids or bases. Wanna whip up a batch?

What you need

- Cooking pan
- Head of red cabbage
- Water
- Grownup helper
- Cup
- Experiment tray
- Dropper
- Household substances (vinegar, baking soda, shampoo, lemon juice, window cleaner, dishwashing liquid, clear soda, or anything else you want to test)

WHAT YOU DO

1. Fill the pan about three-quarters of the way with shredded red cabbage. Add water to about the same level.

2. Ask your grownup helper to put the pan on the stove and bring the water to a boil. Let the water boil for about a minute. Turn off the stove and let the water cool down for about 20 minutes.

3. Pour the water (now purple) into a cup. Throw out the cabbage or give it to your friendly local rat.

4. There are six rounded pits in your experiment tray. Into each pit, put a few drops of any household substance you want to test. (If the substance is solid, dissolve it in a little water first.)

5. Use the dropper to add some Stinky, Cabbage Stew to each indentation. WHOA! You're seeing PINK and GREEN SPOTS!

TRY THIS

For a slower, stove-free method, combine fresh, shredded red cabbage and warm water in a resealable plastic bag. Let the mixture sit overnight or until the water turns purple.

AND NOW THE SCIENTIFIC SCOOP

Cabbage juice turns hot pink in the presence of acids and green in the presence of bases. When you add the juice to the substances in the tray, you can see the colors change! Substances that change color when exposed to acids or bases are called indicators.

45

Spice It Up

After all those nose-holding, disgusting (but fun) smells, I think it's time for some pleasant ones. In this experiment, you're going to make fragrant oil out of some common household spices.

What you need

- **Aromatic spices** (such as cloves, cinnamon, nutmeg, allspice, and ginger)
- **Petri dish**
- **Vegetable oil**
- **Large square of aluminum foil**
- **Desk lamp with a flexible neck**

WHAT YOU DO

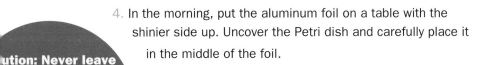

1. Put a variety of spices into the Petri dish. Use whichever ones smell the best to you.

2. Pour vegetable oil into the Petri dish until it just covers the spices.

3. Cover your Petri dish and allow the spices to soak overnight.

4. In the morning, put the aluminum foil on a table with the shinier side up. Uncover the Petri dish and carefully place it in the middle of the foil.

5. Position the desk lamp as shown so that it shines directly into the Petri dish. Then bend up the edges of the aluminum foil. This will reflect as much heat and light as possible into the Petri dish.

6. Wait 10-15 minutes. A delicious, spicy scent will begin to drift through the air. You've made your own aromatic oil!

AND NOW THE SCIENTIFIC SCOOP

As the spices soak in the oil, they release their own essential oils that contain odorants. When you heat the oil in the Petri dish with the desk lamp, these oils become volatile—that is, they vaporize into scented gas that escapes from the Petri dish into the air, and then into your nose.

Perfect Potpourri

To avoid sounding silly (and that's the last thing a scientist wants), make sure you pronounce "potpourri" correctly: POE-pour-EE. This fruity, sweet-smelling concoction is guaranteed to delight your nose.

What you need

- Orange peel
- Lemon peel
- Cookie sheet
- Grownup helper
- Knife
- Apple
- Resealable plastic bag
- Small and large measuring spoons
- **Nutmeg** (or other sweet-smelling spice)
- **Salt**

WHAT YOU DO

1. Peel the orange and the lemon, shredding the peel into small pieces as you go. Set the pieces on the cookie sheet.

2. Have your grownup helper cut the apple into small pieces. Add these pieces to the pile on the cookie sheet.

3. Spread the fruit parts around on the cookie sheet so they form a thin layer. Then ask your helper to turn the oven on to 250°F (120°C) and put the cookie sheet into the oven.

4. Let the mixture bake until it's dry. (This will probably take a couple of hours.) With your helper, check the mixture every half-hour or so to see how it's coming along. Remember that you want to dry the mixture, not cook it. It shouldn't sizzle or shrivel too quickly. If it does, your helper should turn the oven temperature down a bit.

5. Ask your helper to take the mixture out of the oven. Let it cool, then put it into a resealable plastic bag. Add one small measuring spoonful of nutmeg and one large measuring spoonful of salt, and then seal the bag and shake well. Allow the mixture to sit overnight.

6. Open the bag and take a whiff. You've made your own potpourri!

AND NOW THE SCIENTIFIC SCOOP

Heating your potpourri mixture in the oven dries it, locking in aromatic oils and preventing it from rotting. The salt also helps the mixture to dry, because salt absorbs moisture. The finished potpourri releases its fragrance slowly, creating a super smell that can last for weeks!

Just Plain Cool Stuff: On the Tip of My Tongue

L ook at your tongue. See anything interesting? Probably not. But it's what you don't see that will disgust you. I TOLD you science was fun!

What you need

- Grownup helper
- Unflavored, unsweetened gelatin
- Petri dish
- Wooden scraper

WHAT YOU DO

1. Ask your grownup helper to prepare the gelatin according to the directions on the package. Do not add sugar or fruit juice to the gelatin. Have your grownup helper pour the gelatin into the Petri dish. Place the gelatin in the refrigerator until firm.

2. As soon as you wake up the next morning, grab the wooden scraper. Gently scrape your tongue from back to front.

3. Use the scraper to spread your tongue gunk onto the gelatin.

4. Cover the Petri dish and place it in a dark closet. Look at the gelatin every day to see what's happening. The longer it's left in the closet, the better your results!

AND NOW THE SCIENTIFIC SCOOP

Your body is home to millions of bacteria. On your tongue, they hide under a thin layer of mucus and leftover particles of food. They eat, live, and grow there. But your spit contains a substance that kills these bacteria. The wooden scraper removes some of the bacteria from your tongue. Without spit to kill them, they multiply out of control on the gelatin!

Sweet Spit

I'm definitely a fan of sugar, although SALTY FOODS are my favorite. But for the sake of this experiment, I'll put aside my preferences and dive right in to the sugar bowl. (Well, not literally. Although that COULD make for a fun experiment in the future.)

What you need

- Large measuring spoon
- Sugar
- Cup
- 2 cotton swabs
- Water
- Paper towel

WHAT YOU DO

1. Scoop out a large measuring spoonful of sugar and put it into the cup.

2. Wet one of the cotton swabs with water and dip it into the sugar.

3. Touch the tip of your tongue with the cotton swab. You should be able to taste the sweet flavor immediately.

4. Repeat Step 2 with the other cotton swab.

5. Stick your tongue out and wipe it dry with the paper towel. Keep your tongue out so that it stays dry.

6. Touch the tip of your tongue with the cotton swab. Does it take longer before you can taste the sweet flavor?

AND NOW THE SCIENTIFIC SCOOP

Besides making food mushy, saliva helps you taste flavors. Food dissolved by saliva produces chemicals. Your taste buds respond to these chemicals and let you know the flavor of the food—sweet, salty, sour, or bitter. If you didn't have saliva, you couldn't dissolve the food, the chemicals couldn't be produced, and your taste buds couldn't taste! That's why you don't taste anything when you dry your tongue.

Tower of Ice

Hey, a "Tower of Ice" sounds like a neat place to live! Although it would be really cold, and you would probably get icicles all over your skin, and your hair would probably freeze.... Okay, bad idea. Let's just do the experiment.

What you need

- Tray of ice cubes
- Plate
- Salt

WHAT YOU DO

1. Take several ice cubes out of the tray.
   Place one on the plate.

2. Sprinkle salt on top of the ice cube.
   Press another ice cube onto the salted
   area. Hold the second cube
   in place for 30 seconds.

3. Continue adding salt and ice cubes
   until your tower topples.

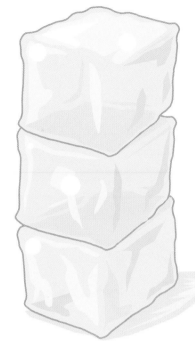

AND NOW THE SCIENTIFIC SCOOP

The salt melts some of the ice, turning it into water. When you place another ice cube over the salt and press down, the water refreezes and joins the cubes together.

Heaving Milk

The milk in this experiment HEAVES and CHURNS in a very un-milklike way. It kind of reminds me of a swamp gone crazy. Hey, one of my cousins moved to the Everglades and became a SWAMP RAT. I wonder if he's ever seen anything like this in the wild?

What you need

- Experiment tray
- Whole milk
- Food coloring
- Dishwashing liquid

WHAT YOU DO

1. Fill one of the rectangular basins in the experiment tray with milk.

2. Put a drop of food coloring into the milk.

3. Put one drop of dishwashing liquid on top of the food coloring. The milk will begin to OOZE all over the place! You can easily see this action because of the food coloring, which SWIRLS AROUND MADLY.

TRY THIS

Use several drops of food coloring in different colors. Space them evenly around the edges of the basin. Put one drop of dishwashing liquid on each drop of food coloring. GASP WITH AWE as a rainbow of swirling colors appears!

AND NOW THE SCIENTIFIC SCOOP

Whole milk contains both water and fat. These substances can't connect on their own. But both substances can connect with the dishwashing liquid. Millions of rapid connections make the milk move. That's why you get the bizarre boiling effect. If you're lucky, it might last as long as half an hour!

Growing Glop

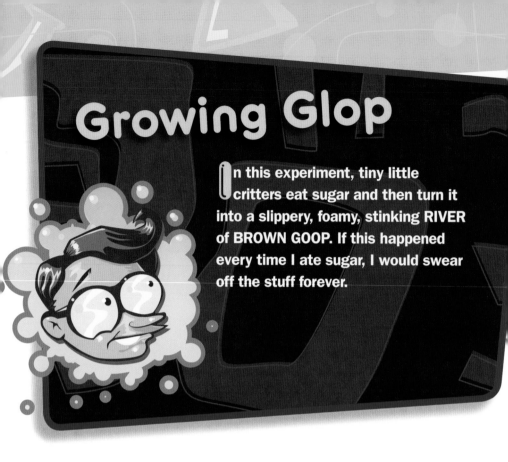

In this experiment, tiny little critters eat sugar and then turn it into a slippery, foamy, stinking RIVER of BROWN GOOP. If this happened every time I ate sugar, I would swear off the stuff forever.

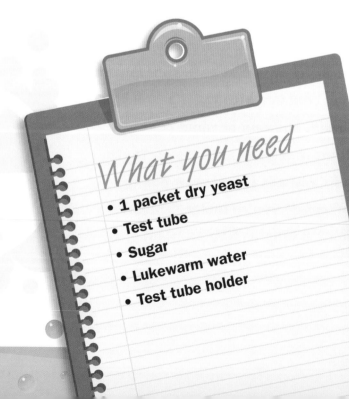

What you need

- 1 packet dry yeast
- Test tube
- Sugar
- Lukewarm water
- Test tube holder

WHAT YOU DO

1. Put yeast into the test tube up to the "2" line.

2. Throw in a big pinch of sugar.

3. Fill the test tube up to the "10" line with lukewarm (NOT HOT!) tap water.

4. Put the test tube in the holder and wait about 10 minutes. EWWWW! A disgusting FROTH grows inside the test tube and eventually overflows down the sides.

TRY THIS

Try the experiment again, but this time, add a little salt to the mixture. Are your results different? They should be. Salt prevents the yeast from growing.

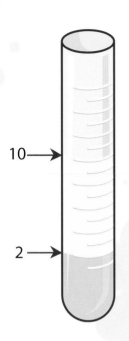

AND NOW THE SCIENTIFIC SCOOP

Yeast is a fungus that eats sugar. As the yeast eats, it breaks down the sugar into alcohol and carbon dioxide. Gas bubbles build up, making the mixture in the test tube expand and eventually overflow. The yeast continues to GOBBLE and SPEW GAS until all the sugar is gone.

Bubbling Bog

The bubbling, hissing liquid in this experiment reminds me of a witch's cauldron. Witches **CREEPED ME OUT** when I was little. I remember hearing stories of witches stealing people's hair and fingernails to use as ingredients in their nasty concoctions. Hey, **YOU'RE** not a witch...are you?

What you need

- Bathroom or kitchen sink
- ½ cup (113 ml) of baking soda
- 1 cup (236 ml) of vinegar
- Bubble solution
- Bubble wand

WHAT YOU DO

1. Close the sink's drain. Dump the baking soda into the sink.

2. Pour the vinegar onto the baking soda. HEEERE WE GO! The liquid erupts into a flurry of fizzing!

3. After the fizzing dies down, blow a bunch of small soap bubbles over the sink. Keep blowing until some bubbles fall into the sink. HEY! They're stopping in midair. What's going on?

TRY THIS

Pretend it's your birthday and there's an imaginary cake in the sink, all ABLAZE with candles. Make a wish and BLOW, BLOW, BLOW! Now, send some more bubbles into the sink. Hmmmm, something seems different here….

AND NOW THE SCIENTIFIC SCOOP

The vinegar and baking soda in the sink react to form carbon dioxide gas. This gas is denser than air, so it stays in the sink instead of escaping upward. The bubbles you blow are denser than air, too, so they sink when you first blow them. But they are not as dense as carbon dioxide. When the bubbles hit the carbon dioxide layer, they float like little round ships on an invisible sea of gas.

Liquid Madness

The weird concoction in this experiment is like a DEMENTED TOY created by a mad scientist. It HEAVES and BUBBLES like some horror-movie prop. Hey, if we're making a movie here, maybe I could be the star! "Newton Goes to Hollywood"—I like the way that sounds. I'd look great on the red carpet, don'tcha think?

What you need

- Light corn syrup
- Clear glass
- Red and blue food coloring
- Small measuring spoon
- Baking soda
- Water
- Vegetable oil
- Disposable cup
- ¼ cup (59 ml) vinegar
- Dropper

WHAT YOU DO

1. Pour corn syrup into a glass until it is about 1 inch (2.5 cm) deep. Add several drops of red food coloring. Mix well.

2. Use the small measuring spoon to drop a few piles of baking soda onto the corn syrup in different places.

3. Gently pour water into the glass until it forms a layer about 1 inch (2.5 cm) deep.

4. Gently pour oil into the glass until it forms a layer about 1 inch (2.5 cm) deep.

5. In a disposable cup, mix the vinegar with several drops of blue food coloring.

6. Use the dropper to add about half the vinegar to the glass. Check it out! BLUE BLOBS form between the oil and water layers!

7. Now use the dropper to pick up more vinegar. Poke the dropper into the glass so the tip is near a wad of baking soda. Squeeze out the vinegar and...WATCH OUT! This is the part of the experiment that puts the MADNESS into the LIQUID!

TRY THIS

Keep squeezing more vinegar near the baking soda wads. Before long your "liquid madness" turns into a weird-looking, foaming, colorful concoction.

AND NOW THE SCIENTIFIC SCOOP

This experiment combines a density gradient with a chemical reaction. Lighter liquids float on top of heavier liquids, creating layers in the glass. The vinegar drops through the oil but has trouble breaking through to the water layer, so blobs of vinegar pile up in a very interesting way. Chemical reactions occur that destroy the balance in the glass and throw everything into TURMOIL!

Sadly, we've come to the end of our experiments. But if you want to keep learning about science, this glossary will help you understand some of the scientific terms and concepts in this book. Until next time, fellow scientists!

Acid: Any chemical compound that gives off positively-charged hydrogen ions when dissolved in water. Acids react with bases to form neutral substances.

Atom: The smallest piece of a chemical element that has all the characteristics of the element.

Base: Any chemical compound that gives off negatively-charged hydroxide ions when dissolved in water. Bases react with acids to form neutral substances.

Casein: The main protein in milk. Pure casein is white and odorless.

Carbon dioxide: A heavy, colorless gas.

Density gradient: Any substance, solid or liquid, in which materials of different densities are separated based on their mass. The most dense material is at the bottom of the density gradient, and the least dense is at the top. Other materials fall into place in between in order of density.

Friction: The force that resists motion between two objects.

Gravity: A force that pulls everything toward the center of the earth.

Hydrogen: An invisible, odorless gas. Hydrogen is the most common element in the universe. Some chemical reactions take hydrogen from water, since each water molecule contains two hydrogen atoms and one oxygen atom. Hydrogen atoms easily lose an electron and become positive ions.

Hydroxide: A negatively-charged ion made of one hydrogen atom and one oxygen atom.

Indicator: A substance that changes in predictable ways when it is exposed to an acid or a base.

Ion: Any atom or group of atoms that have an unequal number of protons and electrons. Ions carry a positive or negative electrical charge depending on whether they have gained or lost electrons.

Molecule: A neutral group of two or more atoms.

Momentum: The force of a moving object.

Odorant: A substance that gives off a scent.

Paraffin: The main ingredient in a type of wax. Some types of paraffin come from petroleum, wood, and coal.

Polymer: A compound that is made of long, chainlike molecules.

Putrefaction: The rotting process of organic matter.